Cattitude

Michael O'Mara Books Limited

Illustrated by
Lulu Mayo

W www.lulumayo.com
f @lulumayoart
@lulu_mayo_art

Edited by Sophie Schrey
Designed by Jack Clucas

The fabulous
cats in this book
were purrfectly
completed by

....

When Cats Get Emotional

A cat's feelings are in its features.

Content

Guilty

Sleepy

Embarrassed

Annoyed

Ecstatic

Confused

Amused

Surprised

Express your own inner-cat emotions below.

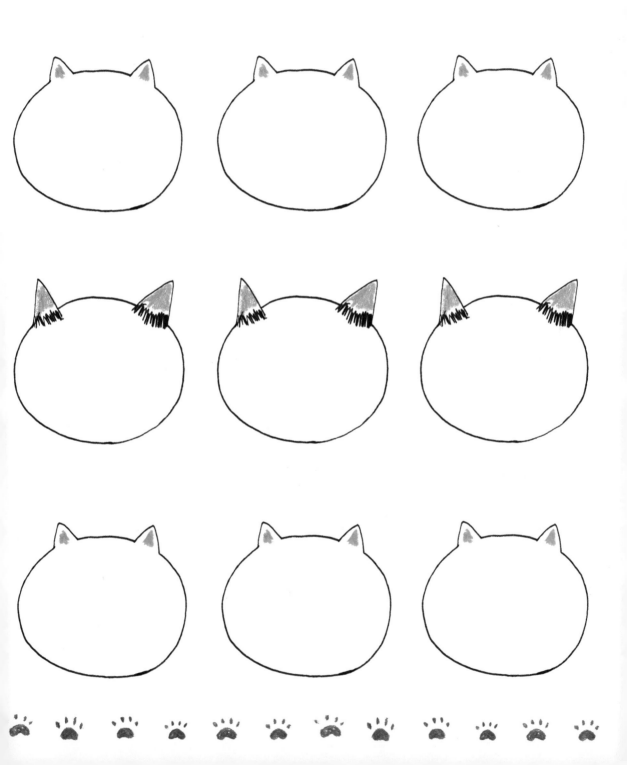

Draw a Fat and Happy Cat

1.

Happy eyes and
a BIG smile.

2.

A round face with
a double chin.

3.

A bow tie.

4.

A round belly and
chubby limbs.

5.

Scribbly tabby fur and a bushy tail.
TA DA! One fat and happy cat.

Draw your fat and happy cat here.

Breeds of Cat

Cats come in all shapes and sizes.
Be bold and colour them in.

Exotic
Shorthair

Birman

Siamese

Persian

Turkish
Van

Pixie-bob

Ragdoll

American
Curl

Munchkin

Norwegian
Forest

Devon
Rex

Scottish
Fold

Very, Very Long Cats

Give these loooong cats funky-coloured fur.

Complete these long cats ... don't forget to give them tails.

Celebrity Makeover

When cats have stars in their eyes ...

Elvis Presley

Marilyn Monroe

David Bowie

Charlie Chaplin

Who's on your cat A-list?

All Kinds of Cats

Use a black pen to add detail and
bring these cat characters to life.

Lucky Beckoning Cats

Doodle wonderful patterns on their fat bellies.

Add pretty patterned fur and crazy colour.

The National Cat Portrait Gallery

Curate your own cat portrait gallery.

'CATTITUDE'
By Pablo Pi-cat-so

'MIAOW-NA LISA'

Customize their outfits
with patterns and colour
to make these cool cats
picture purrfect.

Halloween Cats

Trick or treat? If you thought cats were cute,
think again ... go dark and colour them in.

Cat Dracula

Turn the page if you dare ...

Get your SPOOK ON and create more Halloween cats.

Epic Hairstyles

These elaborate updos are fit for any feline queen.

Style your own royal updos.

Draw a Persian Cat

1.

Goofy eyes and
a short muzzle.

2.

Add ears and
three frown lines.

3.

Draw a round face
and add a flower.

4.

A round body
with layers of fur.

5.

Dumpy legs.

6.

A bushy tail.

Create your Persian cat here.

Furry Fashionistas

Style these fabulous fashionistas.

Cat Collections

The must-have items for cat lovers everywhere.

Cat cup

Purrfect shade

Puss purse

Kitty money

Furry earrings

Cat comb

Cat pops

Cat towel

Kitty socks

Purring pencil

What's in your cat collection? Design it here.

Fine Dining for Felines

What's on the menu for these hungry cats?

Fill the bowls with delicious treats.

Cats on the Road

Cat transport for any occasion ... all aboard and colour them in.

Tomcat
truck

Miaow
minibus

Kitty carriage

Tabby train

School bus

Use these pages to draw your own cat vehicles.

Super Cats

Cat power! Colour in these superhero cats with super zany colours.

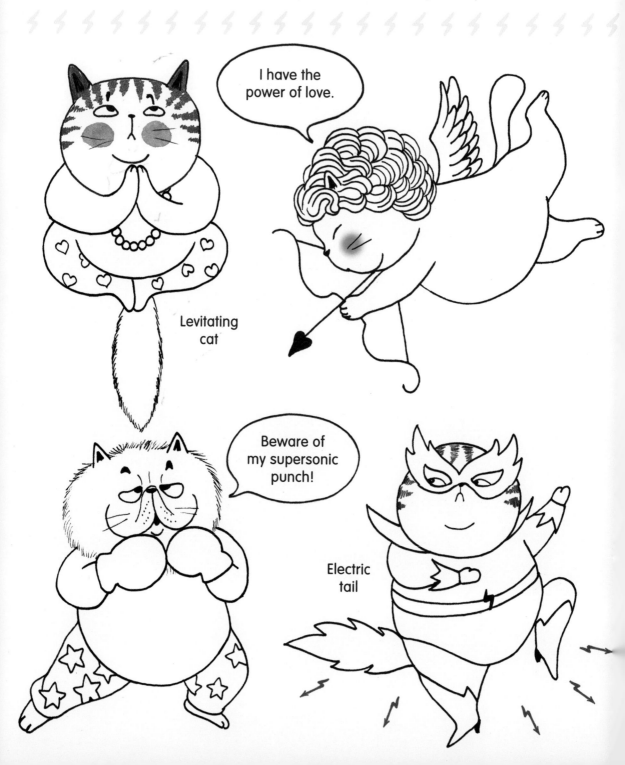

Draw your own super cats. What powers do they have?

Marie Antoinette, Queen of Cats

Marie was one of history's finest fashionistas.

Ooh la la!

Her floral prints were inspired by her love of nature.

Draw your own historical cat characters here.

Cats on Holiday

Every kitty needs to kick back and relax sometimes.
Give these holiday cats a splash of colour!

Cocktail
time!

Cat explorer

Hitting the
slopes

Hawaiian
beach party

Day at the spa

Snorkelling cat

Cat in
the wild

Cat Mash-up

Alpaca-cat

Bamboo sure beats catnip!

Panda-cat

Sheep-cat

Zebra-cat

Complete these crazy cat combinations.

Lion-cat

Lemur-cat

Turtle-cat

Monkey-cat

Draw a Baby Himalayan Cat

1.

Start with the eyes
and a cute nose.

2.

Draw a chubby
face and ears.

3.

Add a bib with
pretty detail.

4.

Draw a cuddly body
with layers of fur.

5.

Now add the finishing
touches on the face,
tail and legs.

Draw your baby Himalayan cat here.

Cats in Hats

Hippie hat

Turkey hat

Russian hat

Viking hat

Witch's hat

Chef's hat

Fancy hat

Magician's hat

Astronaut's helmet

Create some crazy hats for these cats.

Go Cat Crazy

Draw fun patterns and add detail to these cat shapes using a black pen.

Purrfect Beauty

This glamour puss is getting ready for a night on the town. Colour in her beauty kit and accessories.

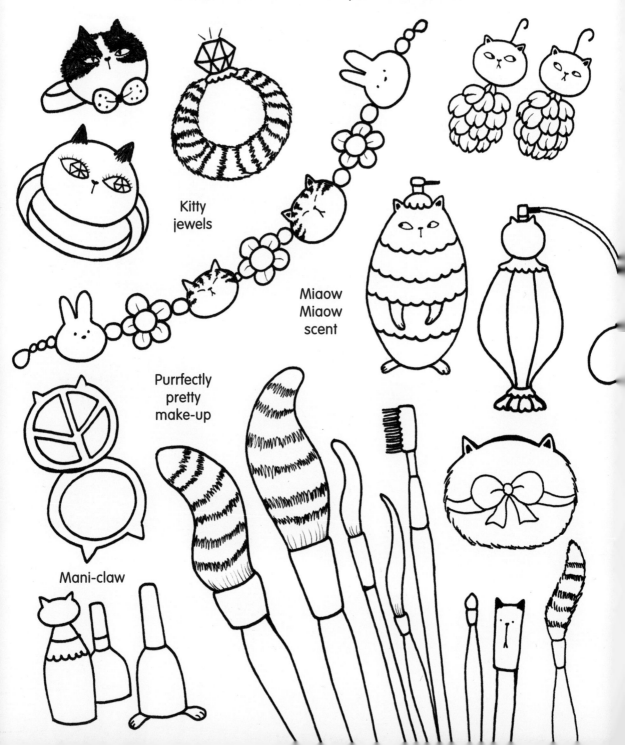

Kitty jewels

Miaow Miaow scent

Purrfectly pretty make-up

Mani-claw

Cat Buildings

Colour in these architectural cats from around the world!

Statue of Liberty,
New York

Big Ben,
London

Saint Basil's Cathedral,
Moscow

The Eiffel Tower,
Paris

Leaning Tower of Pisa,
Italy

Use your towering imagination to complete these cat-inspired buildings.

Dress-up Cats

Your turn. No costume is too cute (or ridiculous).

Draw a Grumpy Munchkin Cat

1.

Angry eyes and a
short muzzle with
an open mouth.

2.

A round face and
pointed ears.

3.

Bushy fur and a
polka-dot bow tie.

4.

Dumpy legs and
a curvy body.

5.

A bushy tail and
splodges of fur.

Draw your grumpy Munchkin cat here.

First published in Great Britain in 2017 by Michael O'Mara Books Limited,
9 Lion Yard, Tremadoc Road, London SW4 7NQ

W   www.mombooks.com
f   Michael O'Mara Books
y   @OMaraBooks

A CIP catalogue record for this book is available from the British Library.

ISBN: 978-1-78243-839-7

2 4 6 8 10 9 7 5 3 1

This book was printed in China.